When Marion Copied

Learning About Plagiarism

By Brook Berg

Illustrations by Nathan Alberg

UpstartBooks™

Fort Atkinson, Wisconsin

Published by UpstartBooks
W5527 State Road 106
P.O. Box 800
Fort Atkinson, Wisconsin 53538-0800
1-800-448-4887

Text © 2006 by Brook Berg
Illustrations © 2006 by Nathan Alberg

*To my dear family, friends, and students at Detroit Lakes Middle School.
Special thanks to Art, Dogfaceboy, and all the Get 'er Done Girls.
—B. B.*

*To the many players behind the scenes—the Bemidji crew, the Poncelets, Ladd and Fowlds, Team Black Dot, J. C., Lamp, ActiFi, and, of course, the Caribou Crew who kept me awake. Thank you to all who have helped me.
—N. A.*

"Did you hear about Grayce and her poem—the one that won the Poetry Slam's Best New Voice Award?" murmurs Marion as she takes a bite from her sandwich.

"Yes! I heard she copied it! She didn't write it herself at all!" whispers Jules.

"Actually, I heard she copied most of it, then changed a few lines, but still she didn't write the whole thing herself," Marion whispers back.

Both girls look across the lunch table at Grayce, who is sitting alone. "I can't believe a person would lie about something like that!" Jules quietly exclaims.

"Oh, I know, that's like cheating from somebody's test, but even worse! It's lying, because you are taking credit for something you didn't totally write," replies Marion as the lunch bell rings.

"I'm so excited," says Marion as they walk into their classroom. "Mr. Owen said he is going to read some of the papers we turned in last week! I hope he reads mine!"

As the students take their seats, Mr. Owen pulls a pile of papers from his briefcase and announces, "As I said this morning, I am going to read some excerpts from your assignments on the beginnings of the Revolutionary War. Please clear your desks. I want you all to listen carefully because afterwards we will be discussing what you heard." Marion and Jules grin and give each other thumbs-up signs before turning to listen.

Mr. Owen begins reading from a paper. "The Revolution, from the colonist's perspective, was caused by England's practice of taxing the colonies without representation in the English parliament. England, on the other hand, saw the taxes levied on the colonies as a common sense way to recover money spent during the French and Indian War, which was fought to defend the colonies. The Sugar Tax of 1764 followed by the Stamp Tax of 1765 …"

Marion sits up straighter. She feels proud. She thinks, it's mine! He is reading my paper!

Then Mr. Owen puts down the first paper and picks up another. He reads, "The Revolution, from the colonist's perspective, was caused by England's practice of taxing the colonies without representation in the English parliament. England, on the other hand …" Marion is shocked! She looks around the room thinking: Who copied from me? How did somebody get my paper?

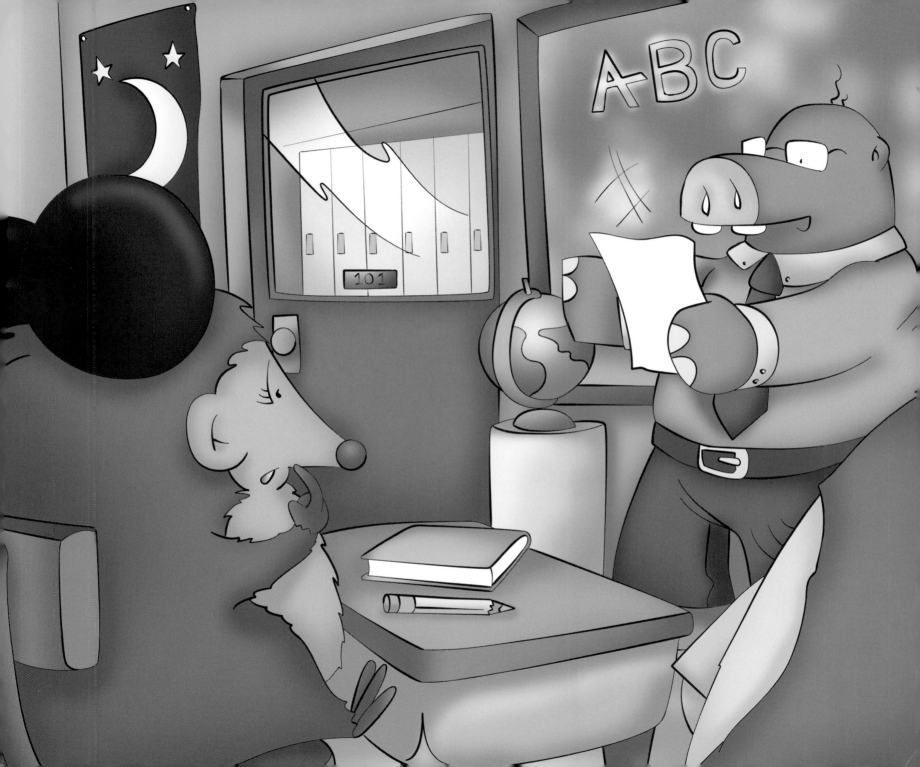

"I have one final paper to read before we discuss them," Mr. Owen says, and he begins reading, "According to Linda Boxer's e-paper titled *The American Revolution,* 'The Revolution, from the colonist's perspective, was caused by England's practice of taxing the colonies without representation in the English parliament. England, on the other hand …'"

Marion shrinks down in her seat. She realizes now that no one had copied from her, but she and the other person had copied from the same Internet site. But isn't that what you're supposed to do when you're researching and writing a paper?

Mr. Owen puts the last paper down, picks up a marker, and writes the word "PLAGIARISM" on the board in capital letters. Then he turns to the class and says, "Okay, what did we hear?"

"Somebody copied," smirks Ernie, "and I wonder who!" Across the aisle, Grayce blushes.

Ignoring Ernie's outburst, Mr. Owen calls on Saul, who has his hand up. "Saul, what did you hear?" asks Mr. Owen.

"Three people copied from the same place, but one of them put in where the words came from," answers Saul.

"That's right," replies Mr. Owen, "and it is an important difference. Give me a show of hands, how many of you normally use the Internet when writing your papers?"

While slowly raising her hand, Marion looks around the classroom and is relieved to see that all the other kids are raising their hands, too.

"And, how many of you," continues Mr. Owen, "have copied things from the Internet into your own papers?" Again, all the kids raise their hands, and Willis asks, "If we don't take information from books and the Internet, how are we supposed to get the information?"

"Ah, good question, Willis, and that is just what we are going to discuss," replies Mr. Owen.

"What we have heard here today is called plagiarism (play-ger-ism), and it is a serious crime," states Mr. Owen sternly. Everyone looks at him with wide, scared eyes while he continues, "Every time you take any part of a book, a paper, or a Web page without the permission of the author, or without telling where it came from, you are stealing. If you turn that in as your own words, or your own thoughts, you are lying, and if you turn it in for a grade, you are cheating."

Marion is so upset that she bursts out, "Are we going to go to jail? I didn't mean to do anything wrong!" Everyone turns to stare at her, shocked that Marion Hedgehog plagiarized.

"You?" sputters Ernie. "You cheated?"

"I didn't mean to," wails Marion, her eyes filling with tears.

"Now, now," Mr. Owen says. "Remember that every one of you raised your hands when I asked if you had copied information from the Internet into your own papers. What we need to focus on now is how to use information without plagiarizing again."

"Mr. Owen," asks Willis, raising his hand, "will you tell us who wrote the paper that told where the information came from?"

Mr. Owen looks out into the classroom and nods, then Grayce stands up and says, "It was me. I cited my source."

Then she walks to the front of the class and explains, "I know everyone has heard about the poem I turned in last month and that it wasn't completely mine. I used the first part of a poem that I found in an old book of my aunt's, but I wrote the last half myself. I didn't know that I had plagiarized until someone called me to the office. That's when I learned how not to plagiarize ever again."

"Thanks, Grayce," says Mr. Owen as Grayce takes her seat. "There are a couple of simple things you can do so that you won't be guilty of plagiarizing. First, you can read through the material, then close the book or turn off the Internet and write about what you just read. We have practiced summarizing in Language Arts, and you can do that with what you read for any assignment."

"Mr. Owen," interrupts Jules, raising her hand.

"Yes, Jules?" replies Mr. Owen.

Jules continues, "That is so hard to do because when I read something I can't think of a better way to say it. I don't have the right words."

"You're not alone in that thinking," replies Mr. Owen, "and it leads us to the next way you can use information straight from another author. When an author's words seem better than your own, or when you use someone else's words mixed in with some of your own, like in a summary, you should figure out a way to put the author's name and the name of your source into your paragraph—the way Grayce did in her American Revolution paper. But there will still be times when you want to use the exact words from another author. To do that you must start by putting quotation marks around the exact words you use."

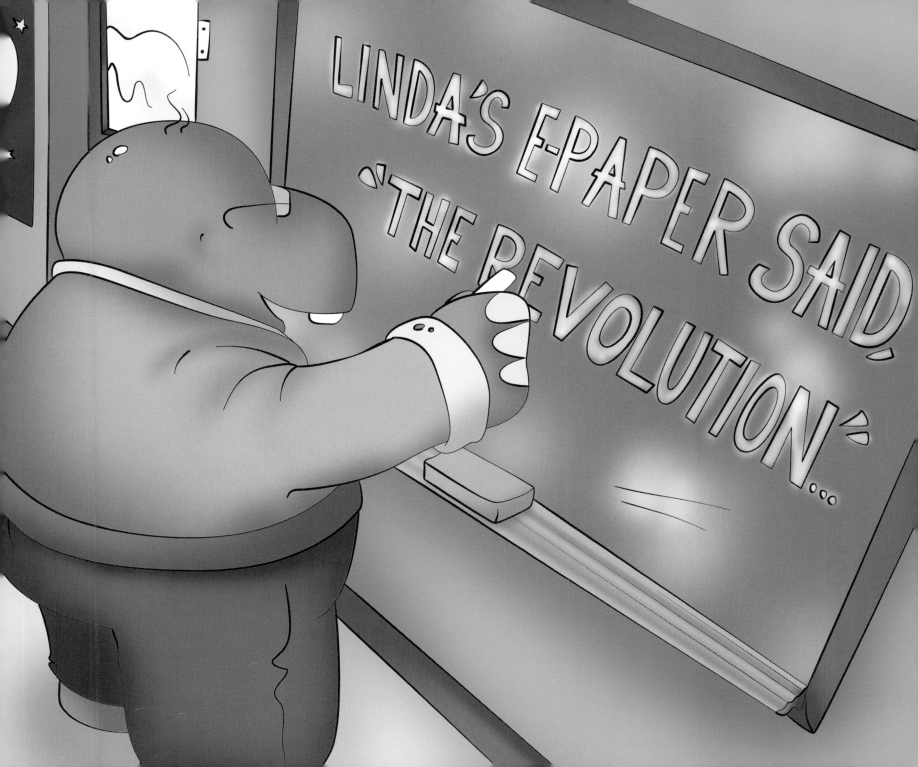

"But I thought quotation marks were used when someone is talking," says Marion.

"They are, and since you are using the writer's exact words in your paper, the original author is talking. Whenever you use a direct quote, you must also cite your source. In other words, include a list of Internet sites, books, magazines, encyclopedias, and other sources you used. That list is called a 'Works Cited' list. People also call it a 'bibliography'."

"Won't people think you're cheating or dumb when you use quotes?" asks Ernie.

"Well," replies Mr. Owen, "there is a limit to the number of quotes you should use in your papers. After all, I want to know what you are thinking—not just what other authors thought. You should always try to summarize first and use quotes only to help illustrate a particular point."

"If there are no more questions," says Mr. Owen, "let's head for the Library Media Center, where Mrs. Carlson is going to help us learn how to correctly cite sources and you will get a chance to practice."

"Grayce, wait up," cries Marion, as she and Jules hurry to catch up to her. "I'm sorry that you got in trouble for plagiarizing your poem. I guess we have all been guilty of the same thing."

"Yes," says Grayce, "plagiarizing really is lying, cheating, and stealing all rolled up into one, and I will never do that again!"

"Me either!" echo Jules and Marion as the three hurry hand in hand into the media center.

About Brook Berg and Marion Hedgehog

Brook Berg is the Library Media Specialist in Detroit Lakes, a small town in northern Minnesota. She spends her days at Detroit Lakes Middle School, where she teaches students how to find the information and the books they need.

Marion was a real hedgehog who lived with Brook for many years. She often visited the Magelssen Elementary School library, where students voted to name her Marion, after Marian the Librarian from *The Music Man.* Marion went to Hedgehog Heaven in 2001.

Brook is the author of *What Happened to Marion's Book?, What Marion Taught Willis,* and *When Marion Copied* from UpstartBooks.

Marion Hedgehog, the inspiration.